Marni Fogelson

A Cello Named Pablo

How Amit Peled came to play Pablo Casals' Favorite Cello

To Endre Silje

Illustrations by Avi Katz

CTM CLASSICS

This book is dedicated to Marta Casals-Istomin

Author: Marni Fogelson

Illustrator: Avi Katz

Graphic Deisgner: Itamar Katz

Compositor: Tom Zebovitz at AlacrityAT

Library of Congress Cataloging-in-Publication Data

The CIP data for this book can be found on the Library of Congress website (loc.gov).

Hardback: 978-0-9992531-0-6

E-Book: 978-0-9992531-1-3

Hello there! No, down here! It's me talking to you, my young friend, not the gentleman behind me. Haven't you ever seen a talking cello before?

No? Well, perhaps not, but I am not just any old cello. I even have a name: Pablo.

I am actually very old: 300 years!
I was carefully crafted by the master
instrument maker Matteo Goffriller in a
studio in Venice with a beautiful view of
the canal. As soon as I got a glimpse of
the world, I knew I wanted to explore it.

Quite a few talented musicians have played me throughout my life. One was named Pablo, like me. Pablo Casals is now known as one of the greatest cello players in history, a "maestro" or master of music.

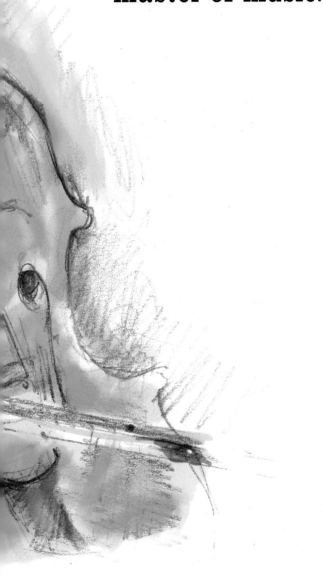

But once, he was just a boy in Spain learning to play an instrument. Many instruments in fact.

His first cello was not me. It was not even a cello. Pablo learned to play the cello by using a gourd!

Later when Pablo finally met me,
we became very close. He had other
cellos, but I was his favorite. For
more than fifty years, we traveled
the world together, playing for
royalty, presidents, and music lovers.
Pablo called me his oldest and
dearest friend. We made such
beautiful music together.

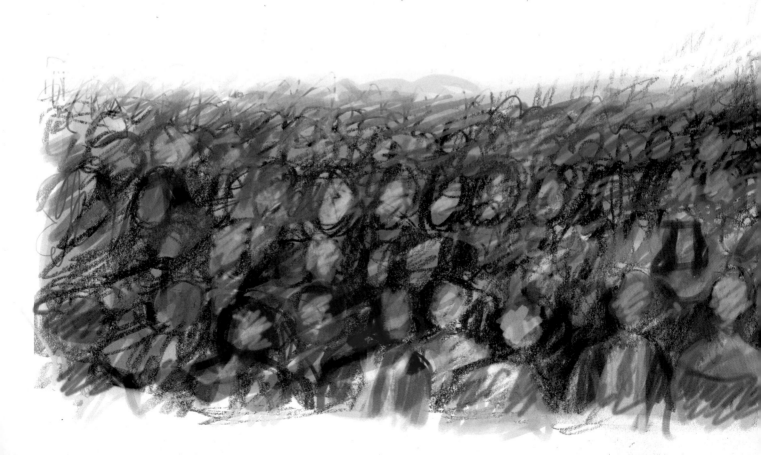

I was very sad when Pablo died as an old man. I can still feel the way his fingers flew like birds over me. I can still smell the pipe he used to smoke during his many hours of practicing.

Pablo's wife Marta is a musician too,
and she took very good care of me.

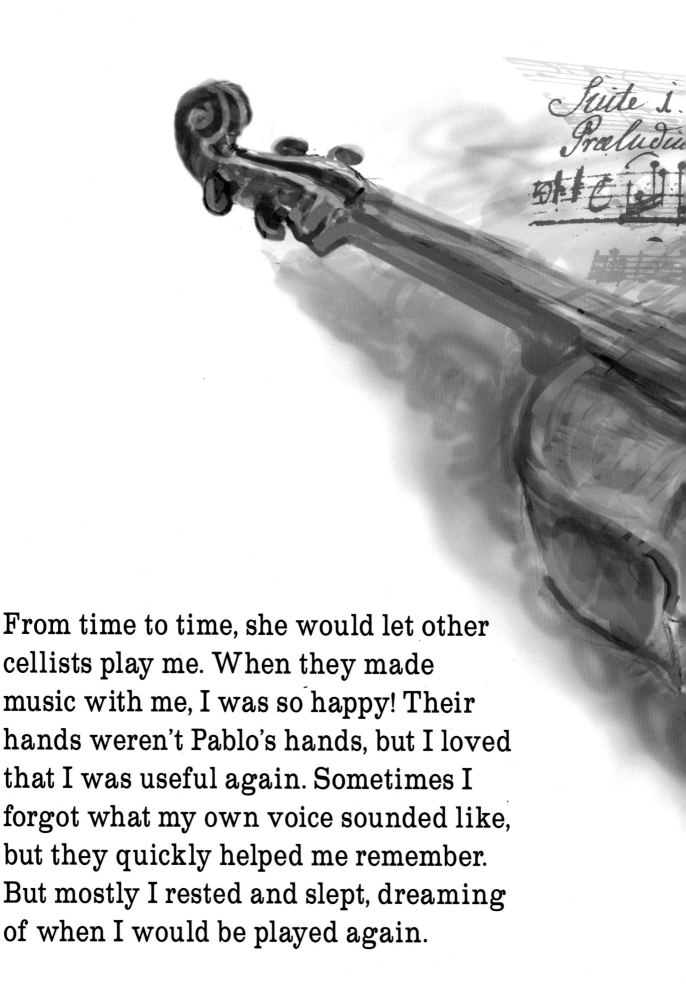

From time to time, she would let other
cellists play me. When they made
music with me, I was so happy! Their
hands weren't Pablo's hands, but I loved
that I was useful again. Sometimes I
forgot what my own voice sounded like,
but they quickly helped me remember.
But mostly I rested and slept, dreaming
of when I would be played again.

During those many years when I was quiet, a boy named Amit was growing up in Israel. He was more interested in playing basketball than playing an instrument, but he liked a girl who was learning to play the cello. He was too shy to talk to her, so he began taking cello lessons too.

Instead of falling in love with the girl, he fell in love with music. He listened to recordings that Pablo and I had made together over and over. I guess you could even say Amit fell in love with me.

Just like Pablo had a century before, Amit studied, worked, and practiced hard. He moved to the United States and became a teacher and a maestro himself.

After some time, Marta heard about
Amit and invited him to play me. In the
beginning, we were both a little nervous,
but we soon realized that we made a good
match. Another day, Amit came back and
played me again. And again.

Finally, Marta told Amit that he could borrow me. Amit and I were both very excited to play together on stages around the world!

Since it had been a few hundred years since my last tune-up, I needed a little makeover. Expert cello doctors, called luthiers, opened me up and pulled me apart and then put me back together again. Soon, my voice was as good as new. Better and stronger than ever.

Now I know Amit's hands well, just as I
once knew Pablo's. When we play the old
songs I used to share with Pablo and the
audience listens and cheers, I feel as if I
might burst with joy.
Music is not only about playing notes
or chords, symphonies or sonatas. Music
tells a feeling, a story, a life.

I may look like humble wood
and strings, but I get to
share my life and the lives of
everyone who has ever touched
me each time I make a sound.

One day, another boy or girl will fall
in love with music and take me around
the world. Maybe that boy or girl could
be you. Who knows what you will
find if you only pick me up and play?

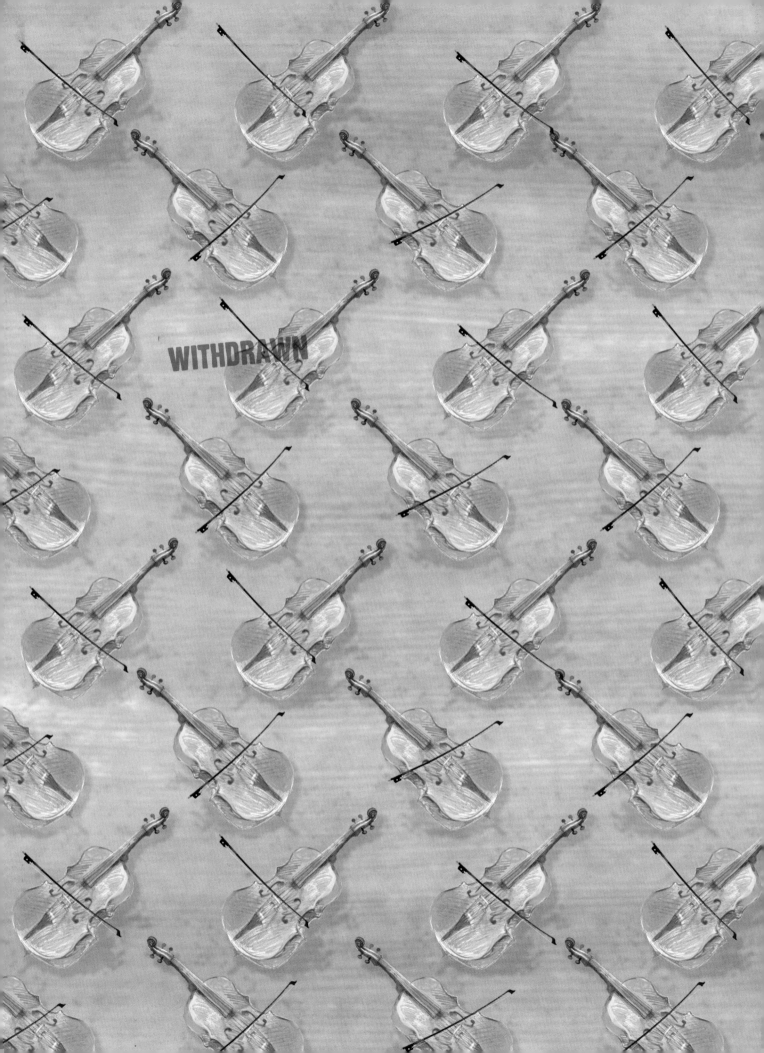